Once upon a time, there was a little bunny named Max.
He lived with his big sister, Ruby.

One day, Ruby was very hungry.
She gave Max three coins.
"Take these coins to the market and get us something to eat," she said.

Max took the three coins.
He grabbed his red rubber elephant and left the house.

At the market, there were many yummy fruits and vegetables.
Max didn't know which to choose!

"Hello there, Max," said Mr. Piazza.
"Are you looking for something good?"
Max nodded his head yes.

"I've got just the thing," said Mr. Piazza.
He opened his hand.

"Beans," said Mr. Piazza.
Max didn't like beans.

"But not ordinary beans," said Mr. Piazza.
"These beans are magic!"

Max didn't like beans, but he loved magic.
He took out his three coins to pay for the beans.

"Well, Max, I'll let you have these magic beans," said Mr. Piazza.
"But it'll cost you those three coins – and your red rubber elephant."

"Beans!" said Max.
Max paid Mr. Piazza, took the beans and left the store.

When Max got home, Ruby was waiting for him.
"I'm so glad you're back, Max," she said.
"What did you get from the market?"

Max opened his hands.
"Beans!" said Max.

"You spent our money and traded your red rubber elephant
for three little beans?" asked Ruby.

Ruby took the beans from Max.
She walked outside.
Max followed.

"Magic," said Max.
"I think you've been tricked, Max," said Ruby.
"There's no such thing as magic beans."

Ruby threw the beans on the ground.
"Beans," said Max.
But Ruby took Max back into the house.

That night, while Max and Ruby slept, the beans started to grow.
And grow and grow and grow.

They grew into a giant beanstalk!

The next morning, Max woke up early and went outside.
He saw the giant beanstalk.
"Beans!" said Max.

Max started to climb the beanstalk.
He climbed and climbed and climbed until he reached the top.

In the clouds he found baskets of fruit and vegetables.
He found baskets of his favourite candies.
And he found a brand-new red rubber elephant.

Max picked up a basket of food and the red rubber elephant.
He climbed back down the beanstalk.
Ruby stood at the bottom waiting for him.

"I can't believe you found all this food!" Ruby said.
"I guess they really were magic…"
"Beans!" said Max.